Lunchtime Games

PHOTOGRAPHED BY

Tom McCrae

SERIES AUTHORS

Lillian Blakey, Mira Hattiangadi, Shirley Stanton

CONSULTANTS

Nora Allingham, Linda Nosbush, Elizabeth Parchment, Gina Rae, Win Sebelius

GINN

Ginn Publishing Canada Inc.

My friends and I play games
at lunchtime.

Atia is playing a computer game.
She is playing to get a high score.

Anne is playing baseball with her team. They are playing outdoors.

Harry is playing volleyball with his sister. They are playing indoors.

Ling is playing hockey with his
friends. They are playing loudly.

I am playing checkers with my
teacher. We are playing quietly.

Playing games at lunchtime
is a lot of fun!